At the
CROSSROADS

At the
CROSSROADS

PRESERVING OUR HIGHWAY INVESTMENT

John O'Doherty, NCPP

National Center for Pavement Preservation
at Michigan State University
2857 Jolly Rd., Okemos, MI 48864
www.pavementpreservation.org

Published in 2007 by the National Center for Pavement Preservation, Okemos, MI

13 12 11 10 09 08 07   1 2 3 4 5 6 7 8 9 10

Book and cover design by Sharp Des!gns, Inc., Lansing, MI

Printed and bound in the United States of America.

Contents

Acknowledgments vii

Introduction ix

1 **The Ruin from Within: Our Roadways in Decline** 3
Our Roadway Lifespans 3
Roadway Predictions for 2020 5
The Value Added by Our Roadways 6
Accommodating Road Failure: The Traditional Model 7
The Current State of Our Roads 9

2 **How Did We Get Here?** 13
Our Complex System of Road Ownership and Operation 13
Responsible Ownership of Our Roads: A Balancing Act 16
Our Road Funding and Spending Mosaic 17
Our Road Repair Mindsets: "New is Better"
     and "Worst First" 19

3

A Better Way to Manage Our Roads 23
A New Model for Preserving Our Roads 24
A New Model for Managing Our Road Infrastructure 27
Developing Economic Strategies 32

4

Barriers to Changing the Way We Operate Our Roads 35
The Road Agency Perspective. 35
Marketplace Pressures 36
Public Support. 37
Funding Issues 38

5

The Road Ahead 43
Getting the Message Out 45
Public Education. 46
Legislative Changes 47
A Call to Action 47
Summary 51

Appendix: A Quick Check of Your Highway Network Health . . .53

Notes. 61

About the Author. 65

Acknowledgments

This document is a product of the National Center for Pavement Preservation (NCPP).

- John O'Doherty, NCPP, *Author*
- Kathleen V. McKevitt, *Editor*
- Kathryn Darnell, *Illustrator*

The following individuals have provided input for this document:

- Gerry Eller, Foundation for Pavement Preservation
- Jon Epps, Granite Construction, Inc.
- Larry Galehouse, National Center for Pavement Preservation
- Gerald Geib, Minnesota Department of Transportation
- Keith Herbold (*retired*)
- James Moulthrop, Fugro Consultants, Inc.
- Steve Varnedoe, North Carolina Department of Transportation

1940s

1960s

1980s

Today

ROUGH
ROADS
AHEAD

Introduction

We have written this document to stimulate serious discussion about the nation's highways, including their role, extent, how they are financed, constructed, maintained, and to explore more effective and efficient ways of achieving our transportation objectives. Recognizing that many diverse stakeholders are vitally interested in our highway system, we have sought to understand and, to the extent possible, balance these interests. In doing this, we have focused on the physical system and the processes by which highways are planned, constructed, and maintained rather than on individuals and institutions.

The document should be of greatest interest to policy and decision makers such as elected officials, agency administrators, and senior technical personnel such as engineers and planners who have broad responsibility for making program and project-level decisions.

Chapter 1 provides a brief description of how our present highway system evolved and its importance to the national economy. The chapter also describes the traditional way in which roads deteriorate and gives several illustrations of the present state of the system.

Chapter 2 describes some of the institutional and financing problems we have encountered along the way and attributes some of the problems to our "road repair" mindsets.

Chapter 3 introduces a new paradigm—using a long-term approach treating roads as valuable assets worthy of preservation and managing our roads as networks of interdependent links.

Chapter 4 warns of some of the barriers we should expect to encounter as we change direction, e.g., institutional resistance, marketplace pressures, and our own discomfort with change.

Finally, Chapter 5 makes some suggestions for the future, including educating our decision makers and convincing the public of the need for change.

At the
CROSSROADS

"Why Change?"

1.

The Ruin from Within:
Our Roadways in Decline

".. . 32 percent of America's major roads
are in poor or mediocre condition."[1]

—Transportation Construction Coalition, 2004

Most of us think of a road as something that will last forever. Roads equal permanence. The success of entire civilizations—ancient Rome for example—was based in part on their road systems. In our culture, road construction is heralded with naming ceremonies and other forms of recognition honoring promoters and contractors. Many of us motorists in the United States also think of roads as something automatically provided by "the government." In short, we consider our roads to be permanent, important, and free.

Our Roadway Lifespans

The first national road in our country was created almost 200 years ago, but our current interconnected system of public roads is only about 50 years old (see Exhibit 1). Our roads are now at a critical period in their

EXHIBIT 1. Legislative History of U.S. Highway Construction and Maintenance

1806   President Thomas Jefferson authorizes construction of the National Road from Cumberland, Maryland to Wheeling (then in Virginia). Eventually it is extended to Vandalia, Illinois.

1830s–40s Maintenance of the National Road is turned over to individual states as a series of turnpikes.

1893   Federal Office of Road Inquiry (predecessor of the Federal Highway Administration) is established.

1916   Federal program of aid to state highway agencies for road construction is established.

1930s   Federal government begins planning the U.S. Interstate system.

1956   Highway Trust Fund taxing vehicles and fuel is created to ensure a dependable source of financing for the Interstate System, or—as it is formally known—the Dwight D. Eisenhower National System of Interstate and Defense Highways.

1976   Federal-Aid Highway Act establishes the Interstate 3-R Program for resurfacing, restoring, and rehabilitating lanes on the Interstate System in use for more than five years and not on toll roads. The 3-Rs are added to the definition of road construction and become eligible for federal aid.

1978   Surface Transportation Assistance Act makes the Interstate 3-R Program permanent and requires states to develop an Interstate maintenance program and certify maintenance annually.

1981   Federal-Aid Highway Act expands the Interstate 3-R program to a 4-R program that includes reconstruction.

1991   Intermodal Surface Transportation Efficiency Act establishes the Interstate Maintenance Program to fund reconstruction and preventive maintenance when a state can demonstrate that such work will cost-effectively extend Interstate pavement life.

1995   National Highway System Designation Act facilitates use of federal-aid funds for preventive maintenance of all roads when states can demonstrate that the activity will cost-effectively extend the useful life of a federal aid highway.

2006   SAFETEA-LU enacted at $244.1 billion. This makes the highest level of federal funding to date.

lives—a point at which major decisions affecting their future must be made.

Although the average formally planned life—known as the "design life"—of U.S. roads is approximately 20 years, concrete pavements can last about 40 years and asphalt pavements about 15 years. In practice, their lives can be extended even longer with proactive maintenance programs.[2] These design lives are significantly shorter than those of European roads located in similar climates and carrying comparable traffic volumes.[3]

Roadway Predictions for 2020

Transportation officials are very concerned about the challenge of maintaining and improving the condition and performance of our roads and highways in view of the following future projections for 2020:

- Traffic congestion will increase significantly.

- Total highway freight traffic will increase 65 percent.[4]

- Simply maintaining the average condition and performance of our roads and bridges until then will cost about $76 billion in capital outlay each year—18 percent more than the 2000 highway capital outlay investment.[5] In addition to capital outlay, in 2004 $36.33 billion was expended for maintenance, $32.88 billion for administration, and $8.01 billion for debt retirement.[6]

- Improving the system effectively by then will cost about $107 billion—65 percent more than in 2000.[7]

- Maintaining the 2000 annual highway investment of $64.6 billion until then will increase user travel time, and vehicle operating costs (see Table 1). Roads will deteriorate and road roughness[8] will increase

Average Total Annual Investment (Capital Outlay)	PERCENT CHANGE IN				Funding Level
	HERS*	Total User Costs	Travel Time Costs	Vehicle Operating Costs	
$106.9	$69.1	–3.6%	–6.3%	–0.7%	Improve Highways/Bridges
$75.9	$48.0	0.0%	–1.0%	1.8%	Maintain User Costs
$64.6	$40.6	3.9%	5.0%	3.9%	Maintain Current Spending

TABLE 1. User Costs for Various Funding Levels (in Billions of Year 2000 Dollars) [33]

*HERS = Highway Economic Requirements System

by more than 25 percent, and the amount of pavement with acceptable ride quality will decrease by more than 12 percent.[9]

Furthermore, escalating road work will increasingly impede our ability to move freely on our highway system. Even now, "the majority of our nation's population travels through a work zone at least once every day. It is also estimated that over 80 percent of Federal-aid funds go into products that the public sees and experiences in work zones."[10]

The Value Added by Our Roadways

A good highway system is a critical component of a healthy economy. To serve its purpose, our highway system must be in good physical condition and provide a high degree of connectivity and efficiency. Our highway system is also important to our economy in times of national crisis. After the September 11, 2001, attack on New York's World Trade Center, all modes of moving goods and services in this country suffered short-term disruptions[11] except highways.

The economies of individual states also depend on highways. In fact, the economic prosperity of most states depends more on out-of-state highways than in-state highways. In 1997, about 75 percent of our nation's products (by value) were shipped by truck; 42 percent were shipped out of the originating state, and at least 15 states shipped at least 80 percent of their products by highway.[12]

Investments in our highways also have a significant effect on productivity:[13]

- *Employment.* The Federal Aid Highway Program supported approximately 42,100 full-time jobs per $1 billion of investment in 1996.

- *Production cost savings.* Industries realize as much as 24 cents in production cost savings for each dollar invested in highways (1950–89 figures).

- *Productivity growth.* Our highway network contributes an average of one quarter of the nation's annual productivity growth (1950–89 figures).

- *Social rate of return.* The net social rate of return from our nation's highway network equals or exceeds the 10 percent rate of return on private capital and long-term interest rates (1980–89 figures).[14]

Accommodating Road Failure: The Traditional Model

Since road failures are not generally catastrophic and occur over long periods of time, we don't perceive them until they are very advanced. Today's road managers and engineers—trained according to a model developed over the last 50 years that actually accommodates road failure—view a road's life in five stages: design, construction, slow unattended deterioration, critical structural deterioration, and total structural disintegration (Exhibit 2). In stage one, road designers provide for geometry, dimensions, materials, thickness, and capacity that will allow roads to perform their functions for about 20 years, but in stage two, road construction can range from flawless to shoddy. In either case, when a road is first opened to traffic, it appears to us to be in excellent condition.

Over the first several years of its life—stage three—road pavement and the structure below it start to deteriorate slowly and weaken as a

EXHIBIT 2. Design Life Stages of U.S. Highways

STAGE 1: Design
The formal planning of a roadway. Design provides for a roadway to be physically adequate to perform its planned functions.

STAGE 2: Construction
The act of building a roadway. Results of construction can vary, but the roadway appears to be in excellent condition.

STAGE 3: Slow Deterioration
Roadway pavement and structure begins to weaken as a result of climate and traffic, but the roadway appears to be in good condition.

STAGE 4: Critical Structural Deterioration
Roadway components become fatigued, deterioration accelerates, and roadway structure is damaged. Potholes and visible deformations appear.

STAGE 5: Total Destruction
Roadway pavement begins to disappear.

result of traffic volume, rain, solar radiation, and temperature changes. Deterioration can be slowed by regular preventive maintenance on surfaces and drainage systems, but such measures have often been neglected because road managers believed them to be a normal consequence in the life of a road. Preventive maintenance is now being practiced and accepted by an increasing number of road managers. Even at this stage, a road appears to be in good condition and offers good service to its users. In fact, if we were to observe preventive maintenance being applied to a road at this stage in its life, we might mistakenly think it a waste of public resources.

Eventually pavement and other components of a road become fatigued and deterioration picks up speed—stage four. As the road endures more and more traffic, visible surface damage such as potholes and deformations appear. The ordinary user might still think that the road is serviceable. However, such pavement will inevitably proceed to stage five—total disintegration.

The Current State of Our Roads

At their half-century mark, U.S. roads can be categorized in four states of disrepair:

- **A** *Roads obviously requiring costly reconstruction.* Many paved roads in the United States have not been adequately maintained and their structure is seriously damaged. Although many of them have been superficially repaired to correct the most obvious defects, their basic structural condition has not been addressed. At this point, such roads can only be restored with partial or complete reconstruction costing more than 50 percent of the cost of building a completely new road.

- **B** *Roads needing—but not obviously—immediate surface strengthening to prevent structural damage.* A much larger number of roads in the United States need immediate surface strengthening to keep their basic structure intact for several more years. Such reinforcement will cost between 5 percent and 20 percent of the cost of a new road. If the necessary surface strengthening is not done, these roads will gradually suffer irreversible structural damage and require expensive reconstruction. Despite surface wear, many of us would consider such roads acceptable in appearance and rideability.

• **C** *Roads rapidly—but not obviously—wearing out.* Another large group of roads, assuming they are given adequate routine mainte-

nance, will need strengthening in a few more years to compensate for normal surface wear. Nevertheless, either as a result of insufficient maintenance or because of deficiencies in original construction, or a combination of both, some of these roads are rapidly wearing out and will need surface strengthening much sooner than anticipated. These roads still look good, and only a pavement specialist could detect the symptoms of accelerated wearing.

- **D** *Roads under adequate preventive maintenance programs.* A final group of roads in the United States receive adequate preventive maintenance adapted to traffic volume and type, climate, road type, and other variables. Unfortunately, very few roads fall into this category.

Enemies of the Road

2.

How Did We Get Here?

O ur roads are caught in a vicious cycle. First they are designed and constructed. As they deteriorate they are rehabilitated or reconstructed. When used, pavement preservation techniques are often not applied until serious damage is sustained. Budget shortages, constituent pressures, and public perception often tempt public agencies—who own and operate most of our roads—to fix the worst roads first rather than keep good roads in good condition. Why use scarce resources to fix "good" roads while "bad" roads are deteriorating?

Our Complex System of Road Ownership and Operation

The United States has about 2.6 million miles of paved and 1.4 million miles of unpaved roads (2005 figures). About three-quarters of the paved miles are in rural areas and about one-quarter are in urban areas. Almost all of our nation's paved roads are under the jurisdiction of public agencies—principally states, counties, and municipalities. Federal agencies are responsible for a limited amount of mileage (about 127,000 miles) in national parks and forests, military bases, and sometimes in urban areas (e.g., the George Washington Parkway near Washington, D.C.). Divisions of jurisdictional responsibility are largely historic in origin and change infrequently. (See Tables 2, 3, and 4.)

Even within a political jurisdiction, not all roads are owned and operated by the same agency. They may be owned by government, by special authorities, or by private-sector organizations. For example:

- State departments of transportation own most of our freeways and major arterial roads.

- In many states, counties own and operate systems of roads, some of which carry substantial traffic volumes, especially in urban areas.

- At the local government level, municipalities and townships are responsible for the vast majority of city and subdivision roads and streets.

- Special authorities such as turnpikes and airports own and operate limited mileages.

- The private sector owns and operates some toll facilities and shopping centers, all of which have public-access roads.

Fragmentation of our roads and highways into multiple jurisdictions poses unique problems. Generally, higher level agencies such as states and counties are responsible for roads that serve longer trips and carry the most vehicle miles of travel. Local roads and streets are generally owned by municipalities and mainly serve a collection/distribution function.

Some smaller agencies have unreasonably high (proportional to their total operations) fixed costs as a result of their small size. Moreover, they often lack the skilled personnel and access to up-to-date techniques such

TABLE 2. Total Public Road Length, 2005 (Miles by Ownership) [34]

	URBAN	RURAL	TOTALS
States	144,446	637,366	781,812
Counties	182,696	1,598,718	1,781,414
Municipal	677,682	577,626	1,255,308
Other	14,111	51,765	65,876
Federal	3,790	123,435	127,225
TOTALS	1,022,725	2,988,910	4,011,635

TABLE 3. Unpaved Public Road Length, 2005 (Miles by Ownership) [35]

	URBAN	RURAL	TOTALS
States (SHAs[36])	18	1,768	1,786
Other (Non-SHAs)	1,682	38,990	40,672
Federal	0	691	691
Minor Collector	0	88,957	88,957
Local	43,674	1,232,977	1,276,651
TOTALS	45,374	1,363,383	1,408,757

TABLE 4. Public Road Length, 2005 (Miles by Jurisdiction) [37]

	URBAN	RURAL	TOTAL	PERCENTAGE
Federal[38]	3,790	123,435	127,225	3.17
States	144,446	637,366	781,812	19.49
Counties	182,696	1,598,718	1,781,414	44.41
Municipal	677,682	577,626	1,255,308	31.29
Other[39]	14,111	51,765	65,876	1.64
TOTALS	1,022,725	2,988,910	4,011,635	100.00

as pavement management systems found in many larger organizations. Although their small road systems prevent them from taking advantage of economies of scale, they retain a large measure of control over their facilities.[15]

Despite jurisdictional fragmentation, our roads and highways must operate as a seamless system rather than a series of connected but disjointed links. Motorists are not generally aware of whose facilities they are using but expect uniformly smooth and safe roads.

Responsible Ownership of Our Roads: A Balancing Act

Our roads are essentially held in public trust by their respective agencies and are available for our use without discrimination on the condition that we observe traffic laws and other rules. These agencies have a big job:

- They make decisions about where, what, and when road work activities such as construction and maintenance should be undertaken. Their decisions affect design, contracting of reconstruction or rehabilitation, evaluation, and maintenance of facilities.

- They balance prudent and honest use of resources with public interest in road safety, comfort, quietness, mobility, and expeditious travel times.

- They play an important role in ensuring that our road systems are capable of being modified to meet short- and long-term dynamic demands while also accurately identifying new construction and improvement projects, choosing projects that respond to public needs, minimizing environmental impacts, securing adequate financing, maximizing public benefits, and planning construction to minimize public inconvenience.

- They discharge their responsibilities in an environment of complex rules and regulations largely aimed at preventing fraud and misuse of public funds.

Our Road Funding and Spending Mosaic

About 90 years ago, in 1916, the federal government established a formal program of aid to state highway agencies to construct and improve roads. Funding came from the general fund of the U.S. Treasury. States were required to use their own funds to maintain these projects.

In 1956, the Highway Trust Fund was created[16] primarily to ensure a dependable source of financing for the Dwight D. Eisenhower National System of Interstate and Defense Highways and to continue funding the federal-aid highway program. Certain highway-user (fuel and vehicle) taxes could be credited to the trust fund to finance the highway program. (Although the fund has been extended on a regular basis and all indications are that Congress will continue to do so, there is no guarantee that this will occur. Current legislation extends the imposition of the taxes and their transfer to the trust fund through 30 September 2011.[17])

Between 1945 and 2004, federal, state, and local highway receipts grew from less than $2 billion to more than $145 billion. Spending also increased significantly, reflecting the construction of the Interstate system. Since the Federal-Aid Highway Act added resurfacing and rehabilitation to the definition of road construction in 1976, legislation that provides for funding routine maintenance and reconstruction has continued to evolve (see Exhibit 1, page 4), and funding for highway restoration and rehabilitation has increased. Nonetheless, spending on capital projects continues to exceed spending on operations and maintenance. In 2004, all levels of government spent almost twice as much on capital projects as on operations and maintenance. Whereas local governments spent about 37 percent of their highway funds on capital projects and 40 percent on operations and maintenance,[18] state transportation agencies spent about 61 percent on capital projects and only 18 percent on operations and maintenance. (See Tables 5, 6, and 7, and Figure 1.)

TABLE 5. Highway Receipts by Governmental Unit (Dollars in Billions) [40]

YEAR	FEDERAL	STATE	LOCAL	TOTAL
1945	$0.09	$1.21	$0.62	$1.92
1982	$10.11	$22.08	$11.87	$44.06
2004	$30.91	$72.86	$41.54	$145.31

TABLE 6. Highway Disbursements by Function (Dollars in Billions) [41]

YEAR	CAPITAL OUTLAY	MAINTENANCE	ADMINISTRATIVE[42]	DEBT RETIREMENT	TOTAL
1945	$0.37	$0.80	$0.26	$0.27	$1.70
1982	$19.05	$13.32	$8.91	$1.69	$42.97
2000	$61.32	$30.64	$25.63	$5.11	$122.70
2004	$70.27	$36.33	$32.88	$8.01	$147.49

TABLE 7. Disbursements for Highways, 2005 (by Expending Agencies) [43]

ITEM	MILLIONS OF DOLLARS SPENT BY			TOTALS	
	FEDERAL[44]	STATES	LOCALS	AMOUNTS	PERCENT
Capital Outlay					
State	0	50,309	0	50,309	32.95
Local	0	4,379	19,770	24,149	15.81
Other	704	1	0	705	0.46
SUBTOTALS	704	54,689	19,770	75,162	49.22
Maintenance/Traffic					
State	0	15,944	0	15,944	10.44
Local	0	150	21,449	21,599	14.15
Other	338	1	0	339	0.22
SUBTOTALS	338	16,096	21,449	37,882	24.81
Administration/Research[45]	861	6,523	3,742	11,126	7.29
Law Enforcement/Safety	0	7,522	6,544	14,066	9.21
Debt Interest	0	4,362	2,030	6,392	4.19
Total Disbursements	1,902	89,191	53,535	144,629	94.71
Bond Retirements[46]	0	5,293	2,778	8,071	5.29
GRAND TOTALS	1,902	94,484	56,313	152,700	100.00

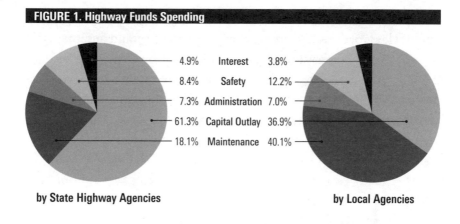

FIGURE 1. Highway Funds Spending

	State Highway Agencies	Local Agencies
Interest	4.9%	3.8%
Safety	8.4%	12.2%
Administration	7.3%	7.0%
Capital Outlay	61.3%	36.9%
Maintenance	18.1%	40.1%

by State Highway Agencies   by Local Agencies

Among our nation's many road jurisdictions, road funding comes from a complex mosaic of federal, state, and local taxes in addition to tolls levied for the use of special facilities such as turnpikes, bridges, and tunnels. Each jurisdiction operates with its own funding and within its own institutional culture. In some cases, a degree of interagency cooperation exists at the technical level, but for the most part operations are ruggedly independent in other ways, including financially.

Our Road Repair Mindsets: "New Is Better" and "Worst First"

Many people regularly practice preventive maintenance to preserve the value of assets such as their homes, furnaces, and automobiles. But when it comes to public infrastructures such as roads and bridges, both road agencies and users tend to be blind to the concept. Road agencies are increasingly coming to view their highway systems as assets worthy of preservation in the same sense as equipment or buildings. These road agencies correctly perceive the negative consequences, such as higher costs, that result from poor maintenance policies and practices. While road construction skills are often plentiful, preservation skills are in short supply, and some managers find it easier to build new roads than keep existing roads in good operating condition.

Many road users, keenly aware of their payment of fuel taxes at the pump, view roads as something the government should automatically provide. Road preservation does not appear to be a pressing issue to them because road deterioration is almost imperceptible to the average person. Finally, both road builders and road users generally associate construction or reconstruction with the idea of progress. Paradoxically, general interest in road preservation appears only when roads have deteriorated to such a degree that serious traffic problems arise.

After many years of use, roads are often in such bad condition that they cannot be maintained. Rebuilding them is costly in terms of use of scarce capital and user inconvenience. States, counties, and municipalities have vast experience in designing and executing new road construction, but most are not adequately prepared for preserving the existing road infrastructure to meet the needs of users and the economy in general.

Road agencies do not have the options available to private companies, which operate in competitive free markets and can set prices that allow them to recover their costs and realize a return on their investment. Businesses may choose not to undertake unprofitable ventures, but road agencies do not have a choice—they are required to operate "unprofitable" facilities. If private companies' sales fail to generate revenues sufficient to cover costs, they may reduce costs, discontinue product lines, or go out of business. Road agencies, on the other hand, are budget-driven—that is, they are allocated annual revenues based on demographic data and the extents of their physical systems. A road agency's funding is based on revenue availability rather than the agency's identified need, and "optimization" can only be attempted within externally set funding limits.

Operating within these constraints, some road agencies have had a strong tendency to use the "worst first" approach—that is, to fix the most seriously and obviously deteriorated parts of their road networks first. They may also have neglected regular maintenance, believing that such neglect would have no negative short-term effects and that any resulting road deterioration would not be obvious to the public. This approach leads to a gradual deterioration of the road network and to an accumulation of overdue or postponed road rehabilitation and reconstruction. Emergency repairs—short-term fixes—are typically superficial and do not address structural damage. Ultimately, failed roads will need to be reconstructed many years earlier than anticipated. Using funds originally budgeted for maintenance on emergency repairs depletes resources available for preserving good roads.

In short, we run the risk of a vicious descending spiral of emergency repairs becoming the standard solution. Recovery from this situation would be very difficult and could result in a growing accumulation of structurally deficient roads.

We Must Manage Our Road Assets

3.

A Better Way to Manage Our Roads

Clearly, we must change the ways we address road deterioration and administer our highway infrastructure. We can no longer afford to blindly accept the validity of a model that was developed to meet the needs of the past.

The traditional model of road operation in the United States has been myopic in two ways:

1. Road agencies wait until road deficiencies become evident even to the untrained observer and then are faced with the options of either doing major rehabilitation or complete reconstruction, both of which are expensive and do not produce sustainability.

2. Road agencies apply maintenance reactively to roads in poor condition rather than proactively to roads still in good condition, which is ineffective in the long run. In other words, the traditional model is reactive instead of proactive.

A New Model for Preserving Our Roads

Planning for the Future

By adopting a preservation model that proactively corrects minor road deficiencies early, our roadway lives can be substantially extended at comparatively low cost. Figure 2 contrasts the traditional model with the pavement preservation model. The first descending curve on the left represents the traditional model, in which unchecked pavement deterioration eventually triggers the need for major road rehabilitation. The wave-like pattern of curves at the top of the figure represents the concept of preservation, in which pavement receives preventive maintenance regularly while still in good condition.

Note that the cumulative effect of preservation treatments is to postpone the inevitable reconstruction. However, over the time period when a reactive policy would normally trigger a major rehabilitation, the sum of the present values of proactive preventive maintenance treatments is substantially less than the present value of the major rehabilitation. Moreover, by changing to a proactive, preventive mode of operation, road agencies would be able to predict planned budget expenditures with considerable certainty and avoid the randomness of road repair that now characterizes the system.

Road operation in Europe can serve as a valuable example. Many villages and small towns, particularly in Belgium and France, are connected by roads that were paved in the 1930s or 1940s.[19] These roads have never been reconstructed or rehabilitated. Expensive demolition or removal of failed sections has never been necessary. In rural areas, where there has been only a moderate increase in traffic, the roads are still adequate for present needs, and, according to road engineers, they will not need any type of reconstruction or rehabilitation in the foreseeable future.

These roads have endured largely as a result of conservative design and proper and timely preservation comprising surface strengthening and other preventive maintenance measures. Before the first thin layer of pavement was applied to these roads more than 60 years ago, care was

FIGURE 2. The Pavement Preservation Concept

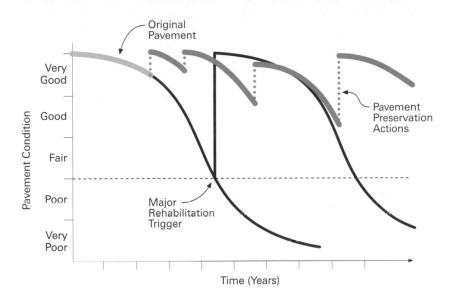

taken to ensure they were properly drained. Several years later, but before the original pavement suffered substantial deterioration, road engineers applied a second relatively low-cost thin layer of pavement over the first. This second layer became somewhat worn but sustained no defects. After several more years, a third thin layer of pavement was applied over the two existing layers. The underlying road structure continued to hold up. Over a period of 60–70 years, these roads have been subjected to as many as 15 or more layers of surface treatments. Now, with pavements up to 40 centimeters (15.75 inches) thick, they are practically indestructible. These roads have been maintained and their surfaces reinforced at relatively low cost.

Obviously, it may not always be possible to maintain these roads with proper preservation treatments. For example, future traffic increases may require that they be reconstructed to increase their capacity. However, the stark contrast between the longevity of these European roads and our own is a serious argument for changing to a long-term, proactive maintenance system as opposed to continuing a reactive system that we have come to accept as "normal" for our roads.

Committing to the Future

When undertaking new construction or major rehabilitation of roads, agency officials expect they will endure and provide a high level of service to the motoring public for many years to come. They do not expect their investment to be wasted. Implicit in their construction decision and expectation is a commitment to apply adequate maintenance to a road as it ages. It would be unreasonable to decide on road construction worth hundreds of millions of dollars without being sure that the roads were worthwhile and should be protected from premature destruction with adequate maintenance.

So why has road preservation in this country been deficient and even nonexistent? By and large, because, in the past, some of those making decisions about our roads have not had a good understanding of the real benefits of sound road preservation practices. Although political factors may ultimately prevail against a decision to opt for preservation, educating our decision makers will result in better decisions.

Decisions have consequences. Once a road is built, management and maintenance issues should be resolved within the political framework after due consideration of the technical needs and mindful of the long-term consequences of funding decisions. Where politically possible, adequate funding should be committed to the long-term preservation of the highway investment. In practical terms, any road agency that fails to commit itself to providing adequate future preventive maintenance for its construction projects jeopardizes the expected longevity of those projects and risks wasting scarce resources.

Characteristics of Efficient Road Preservation Programs

The vast bulk of our nation's highway system has already been constructed and is being gradually worn out by the millions of vehicles that use it each day. We need to put back into the system at least as much as we take out in daily wear and tear. In order to do this effectively, we must establish long-term pavement preservation programs that have the following characteristics:

- Adequate road network preservation not only today and tomorrow, but in the long term

- Optimization of the benefit/cost relationship of the road transport system, which is not the same as trying to spend as little as possible on roads

- Intelligent and cost-effective use of funds

- Minimization of damage to the environment by conserving scarce aggregates and fuel

A New Model for Managing Our Road Infrastructure

If our road systems are to be healthy, accountability and transparency must be built into their management. As public entities, our road agencies do not operate under conditions that are normal and obligatory in the business world. Private companies are:

- *Needs driven.* Private companies plan facilities and operations on the basis of anticipated customer needs. Their costs and revenues are closely scrutinized by investors who expect "reasonable" rates of return on their investments. Our road agencies, on the other hand, must make do with annual revenues allocated to them by policy makers partly on the basis of demographics and system characteristics rather than on customer and investor needs and expectations.[20]

- *Asset driven.* Private companies view their instruments of production—that is, manufacturing and distribution facilities—as depreciable assets. As facilities are used in production, they gradually lose their value. Losses of value are reported as depreciation costs on companies' balance sheets, ending only when residual values reach zero. When they perceive inefficiencies, companies usually pinpoint the problem and find ways to improve. In the past, road agencies generally did not view roads as assets in the business sense and did not generate the information necessary to evaluate the development of road asset value. Today, road agencies are coming to realize the advantages of managing assets and modifying their operations accordingly.

- *Subject to performance measurements.* Private companies have long used periodic evaluation of assets as a tool of performance evaluation. When road networks are poorly managed, the enormous losses go almost unnoticed because performance is seldom measured or reported.

- *Quick adapters.* Private companies are quick to find ways to profitably employ new technology and methods of operations. Like private companies, road agencies employ large numbers of technically skilled employees and, like freight carriers in particular, they operate real-time systems over geographically dispersed areas. Many road agencies, however, have been slow to adapt their network management practices to take advantage of new technology and methods.

Road Asset Value as the Basis for Evaluating Agency Performance

Our nation's road and highway system represents a gigantic investment of $1.75 trillion.[21] Its size rivals or exceeds the value of our electricity or communications systems or of our port infrastructure. Our national road asset is the sum of the resources and elements used directly or indirectly to satisfy our highway mobility needs. It comprises (1) natural resources, including water, the landscape, minerals, and the native forest; and (2) human effort—the sum of the efforts and sacrifices made by present and earlier generations in the construction of our roadways. Because our highway infrastructure is so expensive and took so long to construct, it makes good business sense to preserve it in good operating condition for as long as possible, always striving to postpone the inevitable day when we will need to replace it. It also makes good business sense to evaluate its management.

While it is very difficult to precisely measure the performance of highway agencies quantitatively, it is quite possible to determine fairly accurately the extent to which current reconstruction, rehabilitation, and preservation programs are contributing to network health, i.e., whether network average remaining service life (years) is growing, holding steady, or declining. (The publication "A Quick Check of Your Highway Network Health", Publication No. FHWA-IF-07-006), provides a tool for highway agency managers to assess the needs of their pavement networks and determine the adequacy of their resource allocations. A copy of this publication is shown in the appendix). Other more general measures could include adherence to budget and fiscal responsibility.

Agencies will need to become familiar with and practice asset management. The Governmental Accounting Standards Board has recently issued its Statement 34,[22] (GASB 34—see Exhibit 3) a set of accounting procedures developed to assist state and local governments produce standardized periodic reports of the value of their infrastructure, including roads, highways, and bridges.[23] Agencies will be required to include public infrastructure valuation in their annual financial statements. Uniform financial reports will enable creditors and the public to understand the fiscal operating performance, solvency, and creditworthiness of such agencies. Changing infrastructure values will be indications of how well roads and highways are being preserved by their operating managers. The prospect of public scrutiny should also be a powerful incentive for public officials to do the proper preventive maintenance that will preserve (or increase) the value of their assets.

Correct information is essential for credibility. With roads, many information variables can be collected—physical conditions, traffic volumes, costs, relationships between vehicle operating costs and road infrastructure costs, economic impacts, returns that are possible for various levels of preservation expenditures, etc. Such information may refer not only to the present and past conditions of roads, but also to their future evolution. Knowing certain variables, it is possible to predict the consequences of today's decisions and their impact on road transpor-

EXHIBIT 3. Governmental Accounting Standards Board

The Governmental Accounting Standards Board (GASB) is a private, nonprofit organization established in 1984 by the Financial Accounting Foundation. The Foundation oversees GASB, provides funding, and appoints the members of GASB's board. One of GASB's principal responsibilities is to establish accounting standards—or generally accepted accounting practices (GAAP)—for state and local governments. GASB-34 is GASB Statement 34 entitled "Basic Financial Statements for State and Local Governments."

Although there is no legal requirement that governments follow GAAP, it is generally prudent business practice to do so for two important reasons: (1) Agencies need to obtain clear opinions from their auditors, and (2) following GAAP will likely reduce the cost of issuing debt through general obligation or revenue bonds because bonding organizations want to see true financial conditions.

Compliance with GASB-34 may be achieved in either of two ways, traditional asset depreciation or using a modified approach based on asset preservation.

In the depreciation method, the asset is assumed to be "used up" over a given life. Depreciation is not intended as a measure of actual deterioration and in fact, some assets may increase in value in any given reporting period.

The modified method recognizes that agencies strive to renew their assets and extend their lives. Accordingly, preservation costs are considered to be an appropriate measure for the cost of use because the expenditures necessary to preserve the system in its current condition are reported as period costs.

The modified method is the preferred option because historic costs and depreciation are not effective management tools and because the modified approach uses asset management systems to monitor infrastructure performance and estimate actual maintenance expenditures required to maintain adequate performance.

tation. Estimates of future road conditions can be made according to planned levels of maintenance for existing roads.

The quality of the information generated will largely depend on how much is spent on data collection and the skill with which the data are analyzed and interpreted. Information is of two types: (1) road inventory data describing items such as section lengths, lanes, widths, surface types, structural layers, materials, and surrounding terrain and soil types; and (2) road condition data. For information to be valid, it must be based on solid and objective grounds. In practice, the most common method used for objectivity is to train evaluators to apply uniform technical criteria using standard procedures. Complex technical equipment is also available for automatically measuring certain road characteristics. Although road conditions change constantly, experience has shown that, in normal conditions, annual inspections are sufficient for providing a relatively complete assessment of the state of the roads.

In establishing a successful data management system, road agencies must:

- *Set real and verifiable objectives* specifying an acceptable level of road condition in relation to expenditure. For each road type, this level should be a minimum that is always maintained; for road networks as a whole, this level should be an average.

- *Collect data systematically.* Relevant data should be collected consistently so that on each occasion the same data are recorded for the same location, i.e., data characteristics should be capable of being quantitatively compared for the same physical locations over time.

- *Use compatible equipment and software.* Although this may sound obvious, in the past, insurmountable difficulties have been caused by the use of incompatible equipment and software.

- *Design an expandable system.* The system must be able to accommodate additional data and evolving and more sophisticated collection methods.

Asset management also encourages road managers to consider tradeoffs between short-term reactive maintenance and preservation, between short-term repairs and long-term strategies, and between today's costs and tomorrow's benefits. Historically, agencies have built highways and bridges without due regard for the costs and difficulty of operations and maintenance. Since the start of the Federal Aid Program in 1916, state and local governments have used their own revenues for day-to-day road maintenance and certified their compliance in annual maintenance reports to the federal agency under which they operate. Table 7 (page 18) shows that in 2005, governmental agencies spent almost twice as much on capital projects as on operations and maintenance. In a system that emphasized preservation rather than premature replacement, capital expenditures would decline (as a result of less frequent reconstruction) while maintenance would increase modestly (as a result of increased preservation efforts.) To preserve our investment in highways, operations and maintenance must become priorities.

Developing Economic Strategies

Maintenance Budgets

Public road agencies must have access to the resources necessary to adequately preserve and generally manage road networks. In the traditional "business as usual" model, agencies assume that sufficient resources will always be available to rehabilitate and reconstruct roads as the need arises. From time to time, they use funds allocated for maintenance to perform repairs that become necessary as a result of traffic and climatic factors. Usually these repairs are made after pavements have suffered distress; they do not extend the capital lives of such pavements. Meanwhile, population increases and economic activity continue to grow faster than the resources needed to sustain the system using existing appropriations. Consequently, Congress has had to appropriate ever-increasing resources to maintain the nation's percentage of good roads.

A more economical way of maintaining good roads is to lengthen the time between when they are built and when they need to be reconstructed. Many strategies can be applied. Some involve design changes while others involve slowing down their rates of deterioration. Clearly, some resources will always need to be devoted to building and reconstructing our roads, but if we can extend the time between construction and reconstruction, we will have more resources to devote to other network needs. The expenditure of limited maintenance funds on carefully chosen and timed preservation will eventually yield reconstruction savings substantially in excess of the preservation expenses.[24]

In South America, an economic objective for road preservation has been set[25] as a formula: the annual dollar amount necessary to preserve and manage road networks should be between 2.5 and 3.5 percent of the replacement value of the road network to be maintained. This formula was established to guide "emerging" nations. Research is needed to establish an equivalent formula for North America.

Optimizing Road Networks

Preservation of our roads is an excellent opportunity to take advantage of the potential benefits of network optimization using well established and readily available mathematical optimization techniques. Such techniques[26] can be invaluable in helping decision makers make the hard choices involving individual projects, alternative preservation treatments, and application timing.

Pavement preservation can be implemented on a link-by-link basis or at the network level. Although breaking down a network into a number of component links is clearly necessary to assign appropriate preservation treatments and application times, if each link is considered only in isolation, network optimization opportunities such as economies of scale and link tradeoffs will be lost.

We should seek appropriate preservation treatments for each link in a road network defined by treatment type, cost, and time of application. But optimizing our road system as a whole is not the summation of these treatments. In the optimal solution, appropriate preservation treatments would be specified for each link in such a way that no individual budget or production schedule is exceeded and the total cost of all treatments across all links is minimized. To optimize road networks, every state and metropolitan planning organization will have to reexamine whether to accommodate pressure to widen, upgrade, or build new roads or work as teams to optimize road systems using pavement preservation as a model.

Financial Considerations

4.

Barriers to Changing the Way We Operate Our Roads

everal issues and barriers may arise as an agency develops and implements a pavement preservation program.

The Road Agency Perspective

Issues and barriers from a transportation agency's point of view may include the following:

- *Identifying a champion for the program.* Like any new effort or program within an agency, pavement preservation needs a champion. Without a champion to promote its importance and benefits, new pavement preservation efforts will fail.

- *Dealing with the paradigm shift from worst—to best—first.* Convincing agency personnel to move from the "old familiar" practice of fixing the worst pavement problems first to fixing good pavements while the bad ones continue to deteriorate will involve considerable effort.

- *Gaining commitment from the top management.*[27] The success of any pavement preservation program will require the commitment of top management, including a commitment for dedicated funding and for the resources needed to collect information on the effectiveness of pavement preservation. Pavement preservation projects will not warrant ribbon-cutting ceremonies unless top management recognizes the program's importance.

- *Selecting the right treatment for the right pavement at the right time.* In any new program, a single failure can overshadow hundreds of successes. The right preventive maintenance treatment must be applied to the pavement in a timely manner.

- *Showing early benefits.* Pavement management systems that can show the early effects of preventive maintenance treatments on extending life or on reducing life-cycle costs are essential.

Marketplace Pressures

The issues and barriers to pavement preservation for industry groups mostly involve reluctance to disturb the status quo and include the following:

- *Competition between the suppliers of maintenance and rehabilitation treatments.* Resistance can be expected from suppliers of traditional rehabilitation materials when traditional rehabilitation programs in which pavement overlays are applied every 10 to 20 years change to pavement preservation programs in which new or different treatments are applied. For example, some hot-mix suppliers may resist new cold-mix treatments (slurry seals and chip seals) because of the apparent loss in market share.

- *Competition between various suppliers of maintenance treatments.* When markets have been established for certain types of treatments and a new treatment type is being introduced, industry often attempts to block the new products for technical or business reasons, again to avoid loss of market share.

- *Political lobbying to prevent use of new maintenance treatments.* In some cases, a few industry groups will rely on political lobbying to prevent new technologies from entering the market. Although they may offer technical reasons, they are more likely motivated by the effect on the market if an agency adopts the new technology.

- *Establishing the benefits of new technologies or treatments.* A few suppliers may introduce new technologies without adequate evidence of the benefits. The supplier must provide the agency with detailed documentation of the product's benefits and performance. This is a shared responsibility of both the supplier and the agency.

Public Support

The introduction of preservation programs also affects the traveling public, the ultimate consumer, raising a different set of issues and barriers.

- *Understanding the shift from repairing the worst pavements first to the best pavements first.* Although people understand the importance of maintaining a car or house to prevent the necessity for major repairs, they may not necessarily understand why agencies might work to preserve good roads while holding bad roads together with repairs until resources become available to reconstruct them. Pavement preservation engineers must be able to explain the value of preventive maintenance treatments now compared with the cost of major repairs later.

- *Understanding the effects of various maintenance and rehabilitation strategies on delays and vehicle costs.* Primary benefits of pavement preservation include the potential for reducing traffic delays and congestion by using faster repair techniques and for reducing user costs by maintaining pavement networks in better condition. Although widely acclaimed, these benefits still lack the documentation of national research studies.

- *Understanding safety issues.* Increased safety for the traveling public and for workers in the work zone are other potential benefits of keeping roads in good condition through pavement preservation treatments. These benefits need to be documented and communicated.

Funding Issues

Perceptions of User Fees

It is useful to define the road and highway system as part of a public "service" that is available, in principle, to everyone who wishes to use it. In this way, roads would resemble other public utilities such as electricity, water, and telephone services. It is also necessary to dispel the ideas that roads are a common good provided by the government free of charge from some inexhaustible source and that government will continue to replace them as necessary. Defining roads as a public service helps to reinforce the concept of transparent financing under which the relationship between users and payers is open and obvious, *viz.* that the users (not the government) pay for the roads and are therefore entitled to expect them to be constructed and maintained efficiently and effectively.

Today, our roads and highways receive most of their funding from fuel and vehicle taxes, exemplifying the principle of "user pays." The

TABLE 8. Toll Road Mileage [47]

YEAR	INTERSTATE	NON-INTERSTATE
1993	2,537.30	1,600.50
1995	2,538.20	1,812.51
1997	2,771.60	1,599.30
1999	2,770.40	1,643.34
2001	2,817.30	1,784.56
2003	2,814.30	1,907.53
2005	2,795.30	1,834.62

quantity of our roads is somewhat proportional to demands for their use. In other words, more vehicle miles of travel require more fuel, the purchase of which generates more fuel tax (user fees) that is then channeled back into the system. This is in stark contrast to the situation in most other countries (and several U.S. states) where fuel taxes are diverted to a general fund from which road authorities seek financing by periodically arguing the urgency and necessity of their proposals.

Taxes alone have often been insufficient to finance the large number of roads needed in the United States.[28] In many cases, road agencies have borrowed money by selling bonds to raise the funds needed for initial construction or reconstruction. These bonds were and are being repaid using current revenues. Thus, the companies and individuals who pay taxes today are in fact paying for financing many existing roads.

Tolls are sometimes imposed to pay off bonds used to finance urgently required facilities when conventional funding is unavailable. Despite the motoring public's aversion to paying tolls, between 1993 and 2005, toll road mileage on all roads increased by 12 percent. On roads that are not a part of the Interstate system, the toll mileage increased by 15 percent. (See Table 8). Receipts and disbursements for highway toll facilities are shown in Table 9.

In fact, user tolls would be the most transparent way to finance our roads. When users pay a toll, they make a direct and observable connection between payment and use. Furthermore, tolls are meant to support

TABLE 9. Highway Toll Facilities, Receipts and Disbursements for 2005		
JURISDICTION	RECEIPTS	DISBURSEMENTS
State	$9,730,374,000[48]	$7,897,791,000[49]
Local	$1,731,667,000[50]	$1,729,678,000[51]
TOTALS	$11,462,041,000	$9,627,469,000

only the facility on which they are charged and not subsidize other activities. Generally, however, people have an aversion to paying tolls even when they receive direct benefits.

Funding Continuity

Guaranteeing stable, long-term financing for road preservation is difficult if not impossible when highway revenues are not protected by being deposited and kept in dedicated funds. At the federal level and in many states, we are fortunate in having dedicated funds for providing most of the financing for our road and highway systems.

Operators of local road systems such as counties and municipalities face special funding problems and experience more uncertainty than their counterparts at the state level. Whereas some state highway agencies derive their revenues principally from federal aid and state fuel taxes,[29] counties and municipalities receive some state aid and must make up the balance of their revenues from other sources such as property taxes. This uncertainty makes it very difficult to predict revenues several years ahead—something that must be done if they are to have realistic pavement preservation programs. Consequently, many local road agencies have difficulty establishing long-term strategies and tend to have reactive programs that are determined from year to year by the funding allocations they receive.

The Road Ahead

5.

The Road Ahead

B y now, the thoughtful reader should be thinking that we must change the way we build and manage our highway infrastructure. Serious long-term deterioration of our nation's network of roads and highways raises doubts about the capacity and effectiveness of the traditional way of administering the system. The situation can be compared with trying to fill a tank that has an open drain. While the net liquid flow is inward, the tank will continue to fill and the liquid level will rise. But if the outflow exceeds the inflow, the liquid level will fall. We would like the condition level of the nation's roadways to remain high. Traffic, climatic conditions, and inadequate maintenance practices continue to erode the system, but if we undertake serious preservation measures, we can retard the deterioration without expending substantially increased resources. Alternatively, we can continue our present practices and increase condition levels, but only by massively spending our way ahead of the deterioration.

The first change must be in our attitude – the way we view roads. We must regard them as valuable assets worthy of serious preservation. Other needed changes to shift from our present, reactive approach to a system based on preservation will be procedural and involve restructuring and the way the work is done. For many highway agencies, the transition period will be long, in some cases 20 years or more. During this transition period, agencies will gradually change the mix of programmed projects from mostly rehabilitation/reconstruction/new construction to preservation and new construction.

Funding for preservation will be a major issue in such a transition. "Seed funding" will be necessary to get preservation projects started. If additional funds are not available, resources to finance preservation will need to be found elsewhere, most likely by re-prioritizing highway expenditures. In fact, expenditures on preservation will extend pavement lives and defer the need for rehabilitation/reconstruction. This will release substantially more funding than was used for preservation—$6 to $10 or more could be saved for each $1 spent on preservation.[30] Since preservation will only be performed on structurally sound roads, other roads will be maintained using traditional repair approaches until they are reconstructed, after which they will be preserved using a variety of preservation treatments. Over time, roads will pass through reconstruction and move into the preservation category, and more resources will become available for preservation from savings accruing from longer reconstruction cycles.

The manner in which the transition is accomplished will depend largely on the availability of funding and whether or not additional funds can be obtained to finance preservation activities. In the first case, if an agency can obtain additional funding, it can accelerate a certain amount of rehabilitation/reconstruction, including the associated required preservation. In this way, the agency can speed the transition and begin to realize preservation benefits sooner. Concurrently, its network service level will begin to increase.

Alternatively, agencies that are required to work within existing budgets will not experience transitions as rapidly as those with access to additional funding. Initially, preservation funding will need to come from other parts of an agency's budget until the benefits of longer recon-struction cycles began to accrue. Network service levels will also begin to increase, but more slowly.

Successful transitions will gradually raise network service levels. The end result will be a stable highway system that can be preserved at uniformly high service levels by performing programmed preservation largely funded from existing resources.

Attitudinal changes are extremely important to the success of chang-ing the way roads are operated and managed. Leaders of the effort—the change agents—must be fully committed if they are to implement changes within their organizations successfully.

Getting the Message Out

Change should originate from within road agencies and the highway construction industry, but broad-based external public support will also be necessary. Those who are most likely to favor change are those who are negatively affected by the present state of roads and highways and understand the damage they are causing our nation's economy.

We must persuade those who will favor change to a proactive pre-vention program to play an active role in advocating for change. Interest groups and individual road users would act if they were fully aware of the damage and wasted resources caused by incorrect and insufficient road preservation. Of course before people can have opinions and act, they must be informed. We must undertake communication programs to inform the public about:

- The damage caused by roads in bad condition

- The high cost of deficient preservation in terms of vehicle operation and rehabilitating and rebuilding roads

- The environmental impact of road deterioration and reconstruction

Building awareness of the seriousness of these consequences is imperative.

Public Education

The public in general and affected groups in particular, need to be educated about the ways in which roads and highways have been financed, constructed, and maintained, and that there are far more efficient and effective ways of performing these functions.

First, two dubious assumptions must be dispelled: that roads and highways are provided "free of charge" and that they should only be provided by public agencies. The public must come to understand that roads are financed by fuel taxes and that these fuel taxes are not conventional taxes, but user charges. In fact, user-charge financing is a prerequisite condition if highway funds are to be allocated optimally.

Second, the public must be convinced that some roads that appear to be in good condition are in fact, structurally deficient and that preservation expenditures are warranted long before a road shows visible signs of structural distress.

Unfortunately, we tend to regard road construction / improvements as progressive and desirable and preservation as somewhat unattractive because it lacks the newness and appearance of progress inherent in new construction or major rehabilitation. The word "preservation" suggests stagnation rather than advancement. In today's world, where the pace of change is very rapid, initiatives that do not quickly evolve seem to retreat. In fact, however, lack of proper road preservation is a concealed form of retrogression.

In summary, the public and interest groups need to know that, while their fuel taxes (user charges) certainly pay for the roads, a significant proportion of these resources could be used more effectively and that there are more efficient and effective ways of providing long-lasting, high-quality roads and highways.

Legislative Changes

Several possible legislative approaches may prove useful in initiating and continuing a change toward effective highway preservation. The first step has already been taken. GASB-34 is now effectively mandated as a framework to be used by state and local governmental agencies to account for their stewardship of public infrastructure including roads and highways. Use of the modified reporting method allowed by GASB-34 is meant to ensure that roads are kept at a certain predefined high level of condition. Road agencies that fail to use their resources for effective pavement preservation will be unable to satisfy the reporting requirements of GASB-34, which could result in negative consequences such as lower bond ratings.

Legislative changes could also provide road agencies with incentives to use a portion of their federal aid highway fund allocations for appropriate preservation treatments. Agencies that implement significant effective preservation on their highway systems could be rewarded with additional funding.

Legislation could also encourage the use of innovative road management initiatives, such as out-sourcing certain in-house functions when that would be more efficient and entering into certain public-private operating partnerships.

A portion of the Highway Trust Fund could be designated for financing preservation work and the fuel tax levy could be adjusted periodically to reflect need.

A Call To Action

We must pay urgent attention to three critical areas in advancing the cause for pavement preservation: policy and outreach, research, and funding.

Policy and Outreach

- *Clear definitions, economic analysis, and documentation.* We must define preservation clearly and distinguish it from traditional reactive maintenance. Definition should include documentation of the benefits of pavement preservation programs. We must analyze, understand and promote the relationship between proactive preservation and the life-cycle costs of road and highway systems, including user costs. We need to develop guidelines and strategies for appropriate pavement preservation techniques. A best-practices synthesis or guidebook for pavement preservation would be an excellent outreach tool.

- *Attitude changes from the top down.* Pavement preservation is no longer considered a maintenance program. It is a program employing a network level, long-term strategy that enhances pavement performance by using an integrated, cost-effective set of practices that extend pavement life, improve safety, and meet motorist expectations. To be effective, pavement preservation must become an agency-wide mindset. Commitment to preservation as a priority must start at the top. The Federal Highway Administration (FHWA) must promulgate the message through its divisions before it can be embraced by state and local agencies. FHWA must also send a consistent message to states telling them of their ability to use federal aid to finance preservation programs. We must convince legislators, who provide funding, of the need to move from reactive to proactive maintenance. Pavement preservation should also be part of engineering education and preservation activities factored into pavement design.[31] We must develop an outreach program that reaches all constituents.

- *Process changes.* Business plans must be streamlined and pavement management systems must be updated. The environmental and safety approval process for preservation projects takes too long. A year lost on a job as a result of waiting for approval will set production schedules behind and affect cost-effectiveness. Many pavement management systems do not include maintenance condition mea-

TABLE 10. Examples of Common Forms of Pavement Distress		
DISTRESS	**CAUSE**	**TREATMENT**
Cracks	Environment	Sealing / Filling
Oxidation	Environment	Slurry / Fog Seals
Rutting	Traffic	Milling / Micro-surfacing
Faulting	Traffic	Dowel Bar Retrofit / Diamond Grinding
Polishing	Traffic	Diamond Grinding

sures that detect preservation needs before failure occurs. Integrating preventive preservation into pavement management systems is important in adequately managing a pavement system. Current distress measures and trigger points in pavement management systems are not responsive to pavement preservation needs.[32] Finally, we must identify qualified contractors who can develop and maintain effective pavement preservation programs.

Research

A wide variety of research topics need to be investigated. Following are some examples.

- Integration of preventive maintenance treatments into an overall process of pavement management.

- Appropriateness of specific preventive maintenance treatments under varying pavement distress conditions, e.g., treatment type and timing. Common forms of pavement distress and their usual treatments are shown in Table 10.

- Optimal times to apply preventive maintenance.

- Methods for selecting appropriate treatments.

- Establishment of effective pavement preservation programs.

To be successful, a new approach must be tried to advance the pavement preservation research agenda. The agenda is stalled, not for lack of ideas or interest, but because pavement preservation supporters lack a unified front with which to present their argument to funding agencies.

In this regard, the following steps could be used to develop a unified, realistic, and coherent set of research problem statements and an overall research program that could be funded and implemented expeditiously:

- Conduct one or more national-level workshops to develop a pavement preservation research program for the next five years.

- Identify and obtain the commitment of participants who can make meaningful contributions and help see that the identified research is accomplished successfully.

- Obtain a facilitator to organize the meeting(s) and deliver a final report.

Funding
Funding issues include:

- Ensuring that language is included in re-authorization bills to fund pavement preservation and corresponding education and research efforts.

- Selling the concept of pavement preservation to Future Strategic Highway Research Program and state highway agency CEOs; using the Local Technical Assistance Program Centers to work with local agencies.

- Investigating the feasibility of using state planning and research funds for pavement preservation.

- Using university transportation centers as possible resources.

Time Frames

Roads and highways are long-term investments that deteriorate slowly. The results of changes made today may not become apparent for a long time, perhaps as long as 10 or 20 years. People have a marked preference for actions and changes that will yield short-term benefits. Therefore, changes of the type required for pavement preservation will take a very special commitment and a real understanding of the vast potential benefits to be gained.

Summary

We can arrest and reverse the deterioration of our highway system in two principal ways:

1. We can continue to allocate ever-increasing amounts of scarce tax dollars and try to spend our way out of the problem. By spending enough resources, we can stay ahead of deterioration while improving system quality. To be sustainable, this method requires continuously high expenditures.

2. We can use our present resources in a smarter way: by changing from a build-and-reconstruct process to a build, preserve, and reconstruct process. Such a preservation approach will enable us to increase and sustain our highway system quality within the limits of our present resources.

Pavement preservation is the clear choice for sustaining a strong national economy.

A Quick Check of Your Highway Network Health

by Larry Galehouse, Director, National Center for Pavement Preservation

and Jim Sorenson, Team Leader, FHWA Office of Asset Management

Historically, many highway agency managers and administrators have tended to view their highway systems as simply a collection of projects. By viewing the network in this manner, there is a certain comfort derived from the ability to match pavement actions with their physical/functional needs. However, by only focusing on projects, opportunities for strategically managing entire road networks and asset needs are overlooked. Although the "bottom up" approach is analytically possible, managing networks this way can be a daunting prospect. Instead, road agency administrators have tackled the network problem from the "top down" by allocating budgets and resources based on historic estimates of need. Implicit in this approach, is a belief that the allocated resources will be wisely used and will prove adequate to achieve desirable network service levels.

By using a quick checkup tool, road agency managers and administrators can assess the needs of their network and other highway assets and determine the adequacy of their resource allocation effort. A quick checkup is readily available and can be usefully applied with minimum calculations.

It is essential to know whether present and planned program actions (reconstruction, rehabilitation, and preservation) will produce a net improvement in the condition of the network. However, before the effects of any planned actions to the highway network can be analyzed, some basic concepts should be considered.

Assume that every lane-mile segment of road in the network was rated by the number of years remaining until the end of life (terminal condition). Remember that terminal condition does not mean a failed road; rather, it is a level of deterioration that management has set as a minimum operating condition for that road or network. Consider the rated result of the current network condition, shown in Figure A1.

If no improvements are made for one year, then the number of years remaining until the end of life will decrease by for 1 year for each road segment, except for those stacked at zero. The zero-stack will increase significantly because it maintains its previous balance and also becomes the recipient of those roads having previously been stacked with 1 year remaining. Thus, the entire network will age 1 year to the condition shown in Figure A2, with the net lane-miles in the zero stack raised from 4% to 8% of the network.

Some highway agencies still subscribe to the old practice of assigning their highest priorities to the reconstruction or rehabilitation of the worst roads. This practice of "worst first", that is, continually addressing only those roads in the zero stack, is a proven death spiral strategy because reconstruction and rehabilitation are the most expensive ways to maintain or restore serviceability. Rarely does sufficient funding exist to sustain such a strategy.

The measurable loss of pavement life can be thought of as the network's total lane-miles multiplied by 1 year, that is, *lane-mile-years*. Consider the following quantitative illustration. Suppose your agency's highway network consisted of 4,356 lane-miles. Figure A3 shows that without intervention, it will lose 4,356 lane-mile-years per year.

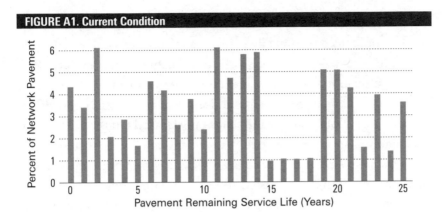

FIGURE A1. Current Condition

FIGURE A2. Condition One Year Later

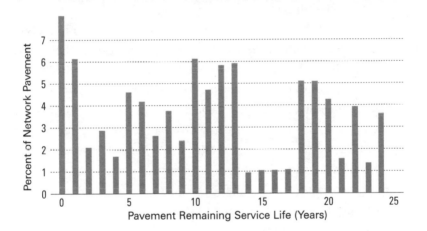

FIGURE A3. Network Lane Miles

Agency Highway Network = 4,356 lane miles

Each year the network will lose

4,356 lane-mile-years

To offset this amount of deterioration over the entire network, the agency would need to annually perform a quantity of work equal to the total number of lane-mile-years lost just to maintain the status quo. Performing a quantity of work that produces fewer than 4,356 new lane-mile-years would lessen the natural decline of the overall network but still fall short of maintaining the status quo. However, if the agency produces more than 4,356 lane-mile-years, it will improve the network.

In the following example, an agency can easily identify the effect of an annual program that consists of reconstruction, rehabilitation, and preservation projects on its network. This assessment involves knowing the only two components for reconstruction and rehabilitation projects: lane miles and design life of each project fix. Figure A4 displays the agency's programmed activities for reconstruction, and Figure A5 displays it for rehabilitation.

When evaluating pavement preservation treatments in this analysis, it is appropriate to think in terms of "extended life" rather than *design life*. The term design life, as used in the reconstruction and rehabilitation tables, relates better to the new pavement's structural adequacy to handle repetitive loadings and environmental factors. This is not the goal of pavement preservation. Each type of treatment/repair has unique benefits that should be targeted to the specific mode of pavement deterioration. This means that life extension depends on factors such as type and severity of distress, traffic volume, environment, and so forth. Figure A6 exhibits the agency's programmed activities for preservation.

To satisfy the needs of its highway network the agency must accomplish 4,356 lane-mile-years of work per year. The agency's program will derive 1,090 lane-mile-years from reconstruction, 1,200 lane-mile-years from rehabilitation, and 412 lane-mile-years from pavement preservation for a total of 2,702 lane-mile-years. Thus, these programmed activities fall short of the minimum required to maintain the status quo and hence would contribute to a net loss in network pavement condition of 1,653 lane-mile-years. The agency's programmed tally is shown in Figure A7.

This exercise can be performed for any pavement network to benchmark its current trend.

FIGURE A4. Reconstruction Evaluation

PROJECT	DESIGN LIFE	LANE-MILES	LANE-MILE-YEARS	LANE-MILE COST	TOTAL COST
#1	25 yrs.	22	550	$463,425	$10,195,350
#2	30 yrs.	18	540	$556,110	$10,009,980
		TOTAL =	1,090		$20,205,330

FIGURE A5. Rehabilitation Evaluation (Projects this year = 3)

PROJECT	DESIGN LIFE	LANE-MILES	LANE-MILE-YEARS	LANE-MILE COST	TOTAL COST
#10	18 yrs	22	396	$263,268	$5,791,896
#11	15 yrs	28	420	$219,390	$6,142,920
#12	12 yrs	32	384	$115,848	$3,707,136
		TOTAL =	1,200		$15,641,952

FIGURE A6. Preservation Evaluation (Projects this year = 5)

PROJECT	DESIGN LIFE	LANE-MILES	LANE-MILE-YEARS	LANE-MILE COST	TOTAL COST
#100	18 yrs	22	396	$263,268	$5,791,896
#101	2 yrs	12	24	$2,562	$30,744
#102	3 yrs	22	66	$7,743	$170,346
#103	5 yrs	26	130	$13,980	$363,480
#104	7 yrs	16	112	$29,750	$476,000
#105	10 yrs	8	80	$54,410	$435,280
		TOTAL =	412		$798,760

FIGURE A7. Network Trend—Programmed Tally

PROGRAMMED ACTIVITY	LANE-MILE-YEARS	TOTAL COST
Reconstruction	1,090	$20,205,330
Rehabilitation	1,200	$15,641,952
Preservation	412	$ 798,760
TOTAL	2,702	$36,646,042
Network Needs (Loss)	−4,356	
DEFICIT	−1,654	

FIGURE A8. Program Modification—Revised R&R Programs

PROGRAMMED ACTIVITY		LANE-MILE-YEARS	COST SAVINGS
Reconstruction	31 lane-miles	820	$5,004,990
	(40 lane-miles)	(1,090)	
Rehabilitation	77 lane-miles	1,125	$1,096,950
	(82 lane-miles)	(1,200)	
Pavement Preservation	(84 lane-miles)	(412)	0
TOTAL =		2,357	$6,101,940
		(2,702)	

By using this approach, it is possible to see how various long-term strategies could be devised and evaluated against a policy objective related to total network condition.

Once the pavement network is benchmarked, an opportunity exists to correct any shortcomings in the programmed tally. A decision must first be made whether to improve the network condition or to just maintain the status quo. This is a management decision and system goal. Continuing with the previous example, a strategy will be proposed to prevent further network deterioration until additional funding is secured.

The first step is to modify the reconstruction and rehabilitation (R&R) programs. An agonizing decision must be made about which projects to defer, eliminate, or phase differently with multi-year activity. In Figure A8, deductions are made in the R&R programs to recover funds for less costly treatments in the pavement preservation program. The result of this decision recovered slightly over $6 million.

Modifying the reconstruction and rehabilitation programs has reduced the number of lane-mile-years added to the network through reconstruction and rehabilitation from 2,702 to 2,357. However, using less costly treatments elsewhere in the network to address roads in better condition will increase the number of lane-mile-years added to the network. A palette of pavement preservation treatments, or mix of fixes, is available to address the network needs at a much lower cost than traditional methods.

FIGURE A9. Network Strategy—New Program Tally

PROGRAMMED ACTIVITY		LANE-MILE-YEARS	TOTAL COST
Reconstruction	(31 lane-miles)	820	$15,200,340
Rehabilitation	(77 lane-miles)	1,125	$14,545,002
Pavement Preservation	(84 lane-miles)	412	$ 798,760
Concrete Resealing	(4 yrs. × 31 lane-miles)	124	$ 979,600
Thin HMA Overlay	(10 yrs. × 16 lane-miles)	160	$ 870,560
Micro-Surfacing	(7 yrs. × 44 lane-miles)	308	$1,309,000
Chip Seal	(5 yrs. × 79 lane-miles)	395	$1,104,420
Crack Seal	(2 yrs. × 506 lane-miles)	1,012	$1,296,372
	TOTAL =	4,356	$36,104,054

Preservation treatments are only suitable if the right treatment is used on the right road at the right time. In Figure A9, the added treatments used include concrete joint resealing, thin hot mix asphalt (HMA) overlay (≤ 1.5 inches), micro-surfacing, chip seal, and crack seal. By knowing the cost per lane-mile and the treatment life-extension, it is possible to create a new strategy (costing $36,104,054) that satisfies the network need. In this example, the agency saved in excess of $500,000 from traditional methods (costing $36,646,042) while erasing the 1,653 lane-mile-year deficit produced by the initial program tally.

In a real-world situation, the highway agency would program its budget to achieve the greatest impact on its network condition. Funds allocated for reconstruction and rehabilitation projects must be viewed as investments in the infrastructure. Conversely, funds directed for preservation projects must be regarded as protecting and preserving past infrastructure investments. Integrating reconstruction, rehabilitation, and preservation in the proper proportions will substantially improve network conditions for the taxpayer while safeguarding the highway investment.

"Remaining Service Life" (RSL) is the tool we need to apply. RSL generally uses data already being collected through the agency's pavement management system (PMS). Construction and rehabilitation costs and performance can generally be pulled from existing databases. Maintenance and preservation data can be estimated until the agency gains actual experience with preservation treatments and integrates maintenance and preservation costs into their PMS.

Notes

1. Transportation Construction Coalition, Letter to Congress, 19 February 2004.

2. "Pavement Preservation Technology in France, South Africa, and Australia," U.S. Department of Transportation, International Technology Program, October 2002, page 22; "Benefits of Rail Freight Study (February 2001)," chapter 3, page 7, figure 3.6 (*http://www.wsdot.wa.gov/rail/plans/DTA/DTAch_three.cfm*).

3. Heavy-duty asphalt pavements are now being designed and built throughout Europe. These pavements have design lives of at least 40 years. Although the initial costs to build them are higher than those of conventional pavements, they will have lower life-cycle costs largely because of the less frequent need to rebuild them.

4. Government Accounting Office (GAO) Report GAO-03-744R, "Trends in Federal and State Capital Investment in Highways," 18 June 2003.

5. Year 2000 dollars.

6. *http://www.fhwa.dot.gov/policy/ohim/hs04/hf.htm* (discht.xls spreadsheet)

7. *http://www.fhwa.dot.gov/policy/2002cpr/Ch7b.htm*

8. Based on the International Roughness Index scale.

9. U.S. Department of Transportation, "2002 Conditions and Performance Report," Executive Summary and Exhibit 9-1.

10. Federal Highway Administration (FHWA): *http://www.fhwa.dot.gov/reports/bestprac .pdf.* "Meeting the Customer's Needs for Mobility and Safety During Construction and Maintenance Operations." Office of Program Quality Coordination, September 1998, page 47.

11. Disruptions lasted for several days.

12. "The Road to Prosperity: The Importance of the Federal Highway Program to the Economic Prosperity of Individual States," prepared by William Buechner, Ph.D., Director of Economics and Research, American Road and Transportation Builders Association, September 1997.

13. FHWA: *http://www.fhwa.dot.gov/policy/empl.htm*

14. Net Social Rate of Return represents net benefits, excluding depreciation.

15. It should be noted that current capital projects are more costly to build as a result of increased environmental awareness, social concern and involvement, and higher design standards. In the current environment, many capital projects are large in scope such as multilane improvements or major interchanges.

16. The Highway Revenue Act of 1956 was actually Title II of the Federal-Aid Highway Act of 1956.

17. On 10 August 2005, President George W. Bush signed the Safe, Accountable, Flexible, Efficient Transportation Equity Act: A Legacy for Users (SAFETEA-LU). SAFETEA-LU extends the imposition of highway-user taxes (at the rates in effect prior to its enactment) through 30 September 2011.

18. FHWA: *http://www.fhwa.dot.gov/policy/ohim/hs02/hf10.htm*

19. "Roads—A New Approach for Road Network Management and Conservation," United Nations Economic Commission for Latin America and the Caribbean, Santiago, Chile, June 1993, page 31.

20. Private-sector managers developing new markets certainly do not have unlimited funding with which to work, but they are expected to have sufficient funds to develop their markets based on prior estimates.

21. FHWA: *http://www.fhwa.dot.gov/rnt4u/ti/asset_management.htm.* In addition, nearly $130 billion is invested annually to preserve and improve the highway system.

22. "Asset Management Primer," U. S. Department of Transportation, Federal Highway Administration, Office of Asset Management, December 1999, page 12.

23. The primary objective of GASB 34 as defined in the Introduction to the Statement is "to enhance the understandability and usefulness of the general purpose external financial reports . . . to the citizenry, legislative and oversight bodies, and investors and creditors."

24. Larry Galehouse, James S. Moulthrop, R. Gary Hicks, "Principles of Pavement Preservation—Definitions, Benefits, Issues, and Barriers," *TR News*, September–October 2003, page 8, figure 2.

25. "Roads—A New Approach for Road Network Management and Conservation," United Nations Economic Commission for Latin America and the Caribbean, Santiago, Chile, June 1993, page 33.

26. Mathematical programming can be used to construct an optimal multiyear program of preservation treatments on pavement links in a network when choices are limited by budgetary, political, or other constraints. Such an optimal program typically maximizes benefits or minimizes costs.

27. Top management will need to commit their agencies to long-term pavement preservation programs. Initially, these programs should be comparatively small and grow as the agency gains experience.

28. The trend toward more fuel-efficient vehicles works against generating sufficient highway revenues from fuel taxes and may result in substantial tax increases to raise the increased revenues needed for future highway construction and operations.

29. The disposition of state fuel taxes varies widely. Some states channel these taxes into dedicated trust funds used to operate their highway agencies. Other states deposit fuel taxes directly into their general funds and disburse revenues to their highway agencies based on priority. Information for individual states may be obtained at *http://www.fhwa.dot.gov/ohim/hwytaxes/2001/tab6_toc.htm*

30. Larry Galehouse, James S. Moulthrop, R. Gary Hicks, "Principles of Pavement Preservation—Definitions, Benefits, Issues, and Barriers," *TR News*, September–October, 2003.

31. AASHTO and other professional organizations are developing courses that meet this need.

32. "Pavement Preservation Compendium," September 2003, Publication No. FHWA-IF-03-21, page 46.

33. "Status of the Nation's Highways, Bridges, and Transit: 2002 Conditions and Performance Report", Chapter 9, Exhibit 9-4

34. FHWA: *http://www.fhwa.dot.gov/policy/ohim/hs05/htm/hm10.htm*

35. FHWA: *http://www.fhwa.dot.gov/policy/ohim/hs05/htm/hm12.htm*

36. State Highway Agencies

37. FHWA: *http://www.fhwa.dot.gov/policy/ohim/hs05/htm/hm10.htm*

38. Roadways in Federal parks, forests, and reservations that are not part of the state and local highway systems

39. Includes state park, state toll, other state agency, other local agency and other roadways not identified by ownership

40. FHWA: *http://www.fhwa.dot.gov/policy/ohim/hs04/htm/reccht.htm*

41. FHWA: *http://www.fhwa.dot.gov/policy/ohim/hs04/htm/discht.htm*

42. Includes Highway Law Enforcement and Bond Interest

43. FHWA: *http://www.fhwa.dot.gov/policy/ohim/hs05/htm/hf10.htm*

44. These expenditures are direct. Other amounts shown as state and local expenditures are in fact federal dollars that have been passed through.

45. Includes small amounts of engineering and equipment costs not charged to capital outlay and maintenance.

46. Proceeds and redemptions of short-term notes and refunding issues are excluded.

47. FHWA: *http://www.fhwa.dot.gov/ohim/tollpage/miletrends.htm#table2*

48. FHWA: *http://www.fhwa.dot.gov/policy/ohim/hs05/htm/sf3b.htm*

49. FHWA: *http://www.fhwa.dot.gov/policy/ohim/hs05/htm/sf4b.htm*

50. FHWA: *http://www.fhwa.dot.gov/policy/ohim/hs05/htm/lgf3b.htm* [2004]

51. FHWA: *http://www.fhwa.dot.gov/policy/ohim/hs05/htm/lgf4b.htm* [2004]

About
the Author

JOHN O'DOHERTY is a registered professional engineer who received his undergraduate degree in Civil Engineering from the Royal Melbourne Institute of Technology (1963) and his Master's Degree (1966) and graduate degree of Civil Engineer from the Massachusetts Institute of Technology.

After graduating from MIT in 1972, Mr. O'Doherty joined the consulting firm of Alan M. Voorhees & Associates where, for four years, he worked on a variety of transportation projects in North America, Europe, and Australia. In 1976, he began a 27-year career with the Michigan Department of Transportation.

For the past three years, Mr. O'Doherty has worked on special projects with the National Center for Pavement Preservation, affiliated with Michigan State University.